THIS ANNUAL BELONGS TO:

MONSTERS ◄ UNIVERSITY ►

1313

_____

Place a photo of yourself here and write your name on the line.

EGMONT
We bring stories to life

First published in Great Britain 2013 by Egmont UK Limited
The Yellow Building, 1 Nicholas Road, London W11 4AN
Activities and story adaptations by Catherine Shoolbred.
Designed by Andrea Philpots.
Monsters University and Monsters, Inc. © 2013 Disney/Pixar

ISBN 978 1 4052 6649 9
54725/1
Printed in Italy

CONTENTS

Welcome to this monster annual! Find out how young Mike and Sulley meet at Monsters University, where they train to be Scarers and enter the terrifying Scare Games. Can they beat the other monsters?

Then, if you're feeling brave enough, read on to discover what Mike and Sulley do next. But be careful, these pages are full of monsters ready to scare you at any time!

Look out for Archie the Scare Pig! He's hidden 10 times in the book.

MONSTERS UNIVERSITY

MIKE WAZOWSKI

Name: Mike Wazowski
Appearance: Tiny, round
Key Features: One eye
Skill: Determination, studies hard
Studying: Scaring

Add green to complete Mike's picture.

Mike's University Diary:

I'm studying hard to be a Scarer, reading all about scare techniques, the history of scaring and top scare moments! I want to pass the School of Scaring and become a Scarer like my heroes at Monsters, Inc. There's one monster I don't like here though. Sulley thinks he's scary because he's big and loud, but there's much more to being a Scarer than that!

Mike

JAMES P. SULLIVAN

Name: James P. Sullivan (a.k.a. 'Sulley')
Appearance: Huge, blue, furry
Key Features: Big teeth
Skill: Loud roar
Studying: Scaring

Sulley's University Diary:

Like my family before me, I've got scariness in my blood! I'm huge and hairy and my roar shakes walls! I don't like that annoying little green monster, Mike. He always knows all the answers to the questions we are asked at the School of Scaring, but he'll never be a real scarer. He's just not loud or scary enough!
Sulley

Sulley

Draw over the lines to write Sulley's name.

WHO'S WHO AT MU:

THE FRATERNITIES

Meet the boy monsters in these three fraternity houses: ROR, JOX and OK!

THE MONSTERS UNIVERSITY HOUSES:

There are 6 houses at MU which take part in the Scare Games; 3 **fraternities** for boy monsters and 3 **sororities** for girl monsters. Which one would you like to join?

OOZMA KAPPA

The monsters of Oozma Kappa aren't very scary, and the other fraternities think they're a bit of a joke. When Mike and Sulley join the OKs, they have to work together as a team to challenge the bigger, scarier monster houses.

Don   Terri   Squishy   Sulley   Mike   Art
             & Terry

Use green to colour their jumpers and make the big OK yellow!

ROAR OMEGA ROAR

The RORs are the scariest monsters on campus! Lead by Johnny, who is smart and ruthless, they're determined to keep their winning streak of the Scare Games. Johnny only let Randy join the RORs because he thinks it's funny that he can disappear.

Join the dots, then colour Johnny's horns to look really scary!

Javier   Chip   Randy   Johnny   Chet   Reggie

JAWS THETA CHI

The JOX are the biggest, most muscle-bound monsters on campus! They love scaring and sports and are never seen without their fancy leather jackets. They'll do anything to win, even if it means cheating! They're really bad losers!

Draw a JOX monster here!

Baboso   Percy   Roy   George   Omar   Dirk

Check out the **SORORITY HOUSES** on page 16!

JOIN THE OKS!

Design your OK T-shirt then decide what your monster name will be!

SULLEY
OOZMA OK KAPPA

MIKE WAZOWSKI
SCARER-IN-TRAINING

OK
OOZMA KAPPA

OK
OOZMA KAPPA

My monster name is:

Can you see which scary shadows these are? Draw lines to match them to the right monsters.

A

B

C

D

1

2

3

4

RΩR

OK

Answers on page 66.

MAZE RACE

Help Mike find his Oozma Kappa teammates and race to Sulley. Make sure you avoid the Roar Omega Roar members, Johnny and Randy.

SCARERs

START

Art

Terri & Terry

Squishy

RΩR

Randy

Don

MONSTERS U.

MU

Johnny

FINISH

OK

Answer on page 66.

Use the small picture as a guide to colour Sulley. Then *ROAR* like him too!

THE SORORITIES

Meet the scary girl monsters in these three sorority houses: PNK, EEK and HSS!

PYTHON NU KAPPA

PNK

The PNK ladies look smiley and pretty but don't be fooled, they're as mean as mean girls get! They can speak to each other using their minds and their eyes light up, which helps them see in the dark!

Taylor   Carrie   Heather   Naomi   Crystal   Britney

PNK

Colour in the PNK logo. You'd better make it pink, or else the PNK girls will get you!

SLUGMA SLUGMA KAPPA

Nothing is more important than scaring to the EEKs. These monster girls have trained together so much that it's almost like they share one brain! They are strong and determined to out-scare any monster out there.

Donna   Debbie   Maria   Carla   Brynn   Violet

Donna's eyes are always hidden. Draw what you think they look like here!

ETA HISS HISS

This house is for pale and angry girl monsters! They are tough as nails and it's rumoured that no one has seen inside their house and survived to tell the tale! Dean Hardscrabble, the terrifying Head of the School of Scaring, is a former HSS member.

Rhonda   Nadya   Rosie   Nancy   Susan   Sonia

Draw another angry monster to join Eta Hiss Hiss.

Check out the **FRATERNITY HOUSES** on page 10!

MONSTERS UNIVERSITY

1. Mike Wazowski is a small, green monster who lives in Monstropolis, the amazing monster world that exists behind children's closet doors.

2. Ever since he was tiny Mike has wanted to be a Scarer, so he can burst through closet doors to scare children and fill scream cans to power Monstropolis.

3. Soon, Mike is old enough to study at the famous School of Scaring at Monster University! There he meets monsters of all shapes and sizes, all of them bigger and louder than he is.

4. Mike quickly becomes rivals with a huge blue monster called Sulley. Sulley can roar louder than anyone and he is quickly invited to join the best house on campus – Roar Omega Roar, the RORs.

5. Sulley and his ROR house friends tease Mike, saying he's too small and quiet to be a Scarer.

6. Sulley is loud and strong, but Mike studies hard and learns everything he can about being a Scarer. He wants to be the greatest Scarer ever!

7. Mike and Sulley constantly compete against each other. They are determined to show each other that they're the best!

8. Before long, it's time for the final exam at the School of Scaring. But just before it starts, Mike and Sulley get into a roaring face-off. And then something awful happens ...

9. As Sulley steps back to give out a HUGE **ROAR**, he knocks over Dean Hardscrabble's legendary scream can, which smashes on the floor! **Oh, no!**

10. The Dean throws both of them out of the Scaring Program. Sulley is then kicked out of Roar Omega Roar house too!

11. The only way that Mike and Sulley can get back into the Scaring Program is if they win the Scare Games. But they can only compete in the games if they're members of a house on campus.

12. The only house that will have them is Oozma Kappa, the house with the least scary students at MU. The OKs live in Squishy's mum's house!

13. Mike doesn't want to be in a team with Sulley, and Sulley doesn't think much of the OKs, but they have no choice.

14. So, following the initiation ceremony, Mike and Sulley join the OKs and get ready to take on the scariest monsters in the Scare Games!

THE END

OOZMA KAPPA

OK

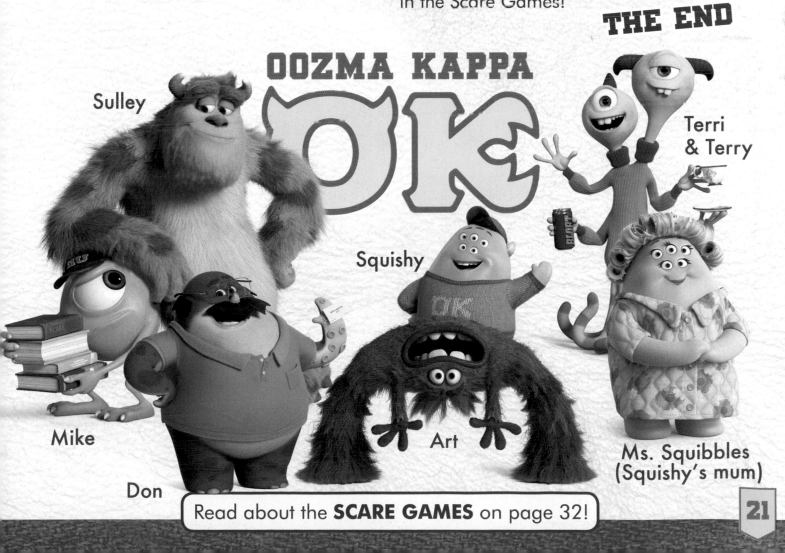

Sulley

Terri & Terry

Squishy

Mike

Art

Ms. Squibbles (Squishy's mum)

Don

Read about the **SCARE GAMES** on page 32!

21

SPOT THE DIFFERENCE

These two pictures look the same but there are 8 changes in picture 2.

Colour in a monster as you spot each difference!

2

23

Answers on page 66.

MONSTER MATCH-UPS

How well do you know the OKs?
See if you can match them to
their close-ups below.

Sulley

Squishy

Don

Terri
& Terry

Art

Mike

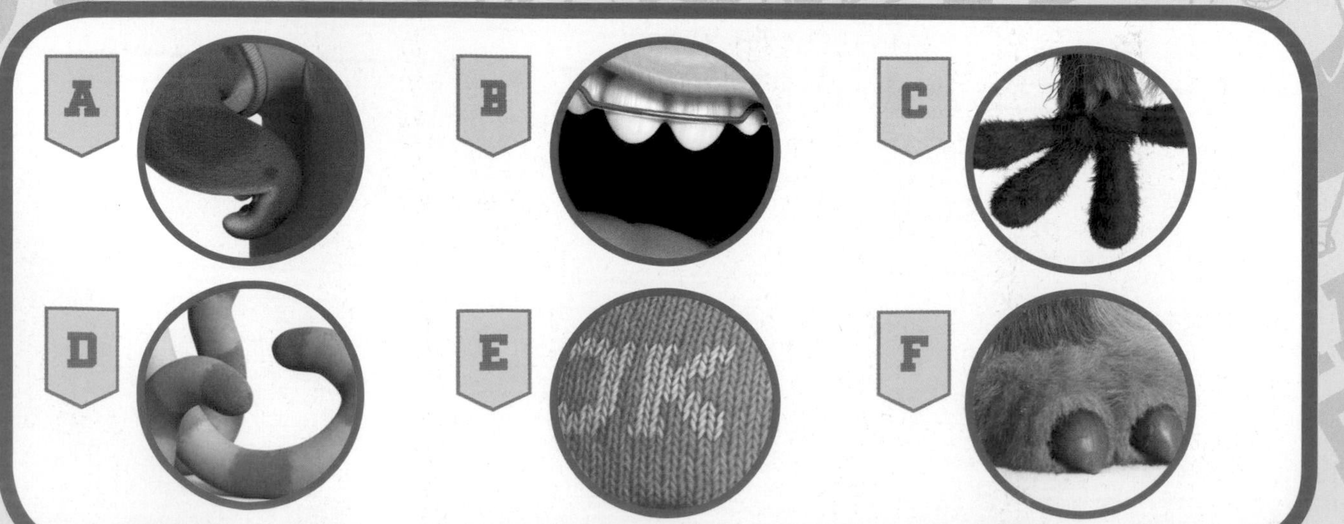

A

B

C

D

E

F

24

Answers on page 66.

Look carefully at this picture. How many of each monster can you count?

Carrie | Don | Johnny | Roy | Carla | Rosie

Add a tick when you find:

Answers on page 66.

See how quickly you can tackle these monster campus activities!

1. JOIN MONSTERS UNIVERSITY

Draw yourself as a scary monster, so you can join Monsters University too!

Tick which monster house you would like to join:

OK   RΩR   JOX   PNK   ΣΣK   HSS

2. FLAG MATCH

Draw lines to match up the monsters to their flags.

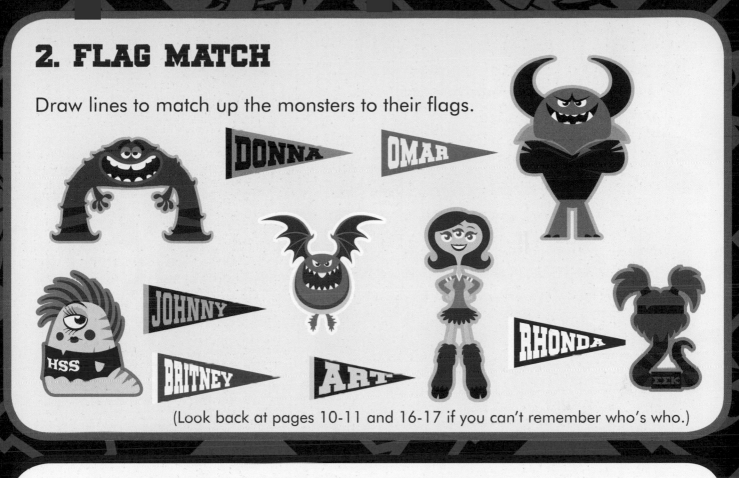

DONNA · OMAR · JOHNNY · BRITNEY · ART · RHONDA · HSS · ΣΣK

(Look back at pages 10-11 and 16-17 if you can't remember who's who.)

3. MONSTER PARTY

Follow the lines to see which MU house is having a party tonight.

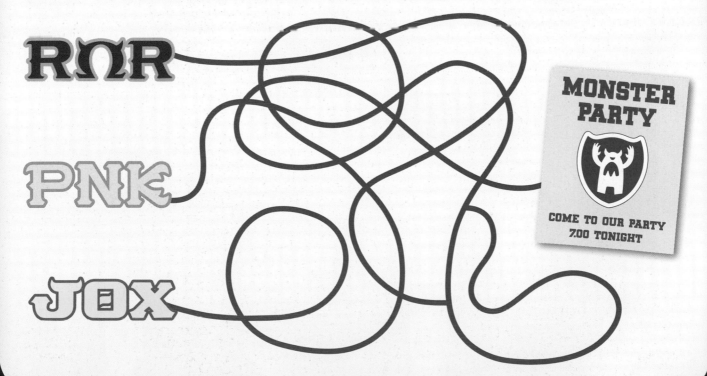

RΩR · PNK · JOX

MONSTER PARTY

COME TO OUR PARTY 7.00 TONIGHT

Answers on page 66.

WHO'S SCARIEST?

Follow the lines to see who are the most and least scary monsters. Write their names below.

A

B

C

D

Most scary

_____

Least scary

_____

Answers on page 66.

28

PROPERTY OF

OOZMA

KAPPA

OK

Circle the monster in each line that's different from the others.

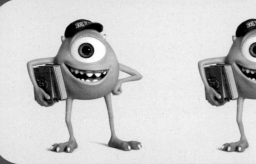  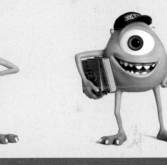

31

Answers on page 66.

Soon, it's time for Dean Hardscrabble to announce the start of the Scare Games! The first event is the **Toxicity Challenge**! The teams race through a dark sewer tunnel avoiding stinging glow urchins!

Mike and Sulley forget about their OK teammates and focus on beating each other. As they cross the finish line they think they're through to the next round, but the whole team has to cross the line together. The OKs are knocked out of the games!

But one of the winning teams is disqualified for cheating, so the OKs are back in the games! Mike tells them that if they want to win, they have to do things his way. Sulley walks away saying, "You tell them what to do, but not me. Later coach."

Next it's the **Avoid the Parent** test. Each team has to get a flag out of the library without getting caught. The OKs manage to get their flag without Sulley's help.

SCARERS

The OKs are thrilled to get an invite to a mid-games party, but when the RORs make fun of them they lose confidence and think about dropping out of the games.

But Mike takes them to Monsters, Inc. to show them that Scarers come in all shapes and sizes. "The best Scarers use their differences to their advantage," he tells them.

Mike and Sulley both admit that they've been acting like jerks. They agree to work together as a team. They train with the OKs and before long they pass both the **Don't Scare the Teen** and the **Hide and Sneak** events. Soon, it's just the OKs against the RORs for the final event!

"Tomorrow **each** of you must prove you are undeniably scary," Dean Hardscrabble tells Sulley, "and I know that **one** of you is not," she adds. Sulley knows she means Mike.

The next day, it's time for the final event of the Scare Games: **Simulated Scare**! The monsters take turns to scare a robot child to fill up scream cans. Sulley asks Mike to go last.

After all the other monsters have done their scares, Mike sneaks across the bedroom to the robot child. Then he gives out a huge **ROAR**, which makes the robot child sit up in bed and **scream** in terror. Everyone cheers as Mike's scare fills his team's scream can to the top. The OKs have won the Scare Games, so they're back in the Scaring Program!

After most monsters have left, Mike goes back to the simulator and says another little 'boo' to the robot child. He's surprised to see the scream can fill up again.

Mike realises Sulley moved the control panel from **difficult** to **easy** for his go. "What was I supposed to do? Let the team fail because you don't have it?" Sulley asks.

Mike wants to prove once and for all that he's scary. He sneaks into the Door Tech Lab, powers up a door and goes through it! As alarms blast, Dean Hardscrabble and guards race to the lab. Mike finds himself in a cabin full of kids. He **ROARS**, but the kids aren't scared. Sulley sneaks past the guards and goes to help Mike. Dean Hardscrabble powers down the door, so Mike and Sulley are stuck there!

Mike and Sulley make a plan to power up the door from their side. When the camp rangers enter the cabin, Mike and Sulley set up a terrifying scare. Then Sulley **ROARS**!

The rangers' screams generate enough energy to power up the door. It **explodes**, blasting Sulley and Mike back into the Door Tech Lab at Monsters University!

It was the **most impressive scare** of all time, but Mike and Sulley are still expelled. However, Dean Hardscrabble lets the other OKs into the Scaring Program.

Mike and Sulley find another way to get to a scare floor at Monsters, Inc. – they get jobs delivering the mail there! They know if they work hard then one day they'll achieve their dream of becoming a scare team, and they will do it **together**!

THE END

Mike and Sulley are all grown up now, and they've finally become a successful scare team at Monsters, Inc.!

Turn over to enjoy their Scarer adventures and see how they have fun with this little girl called Boo!

MEET THE MONSTERS

Who's who at Monsters, Inc. – the top scream factory in the city of Monstropolis!

How many scream cans can you find? Write the number in this box.

SULLEY

Full name: James P. Sullivan
Top Scarer at Monsters, Inc. He's a giant with a big heart to match.

MIKE

Full name: Mike Wazowski
Sulley's best friend and roommate. Mike's quick with the jokes, but serious about the business of scaring.

BOO

Wait – this little girl isn't a monster! When Boo gets loose in Monstropolis, Sulley's in big trouble!

HENRY J. WATERNOOSE, III

Waternoose is the boss at Monsters, Inc. He's been scaring kids for 50 years!

ROZ

Grouchy Roz has to keep an eye on Mike at work – he never fills in his reports properly.

RANDALL BOGGS

This sneaky monster wants to steal Sulley's all-time scare record. Watch out! He can change his colour to hide against any background.

BE A MONSTER

Pretend you are a monster and make a scary noise!

39

Answer on page 66.

THROUGH THE DOOR

Randall is jealous of Sulley's top scare score and will do anything to try and beat it ...

One day, Sulley walked happily out of a door, after another very good scare.

"Well done, Sulley, that's a full can. You'll easily have the top scare score today!" chuckled best friend, Mike.

Randall was jealous of Sulley's success.

"I'm much better than that big ball of blue fur. I should be getting the top scare score," Randall said to himself.

He noticed Mike checking a list for the number of the next door to be brought to Sulley's scare station.

"Sulley gets the top scores because he gets the best doors!" Randall hissed.

So, Randall crept up behind Mike and peeked at the list. The one at the bottom had a red circle around it.

"Why is that door circled? I bet there are extra screams in that bedroom!" Randall said.

Mike jumped with shock. "That's none of your business!" he replied.

Randall frowned. He was sure there was something special about that door.

"If I had that door, I'd get the top scare score," Randall thought.

At lunchtime, everyone got ready to leave the scare floor. Randall quickly made himself invisible and watched Mike leave the list by Sulley's scare station.

When Mike and Sulley had gone, Randall crept over and read the number that was circled.

"Hmm, door 456. That's going to be my lucky number!" he laughed.

Randall rushed to his own scare station and keyed 456 into the control panel. The door silently arrived and Randall turned the handle and stepped inside.

When lunch was over, everyone noticed the door at Randall's station.

"Oh dear! Randall has gone through door 456!" gasped Sulley.

Suddenly, the door burst open and Randall fell out. He was covered in children's clothes and toys.

"That's the messiest room ever!" he cried.

"That's why I circled it, to warn Sulley to be extra careful!" giggled Mike, as the Child Detection Agency appeared.

Mike, Sulley and the other monsters watched as the C.D.A. began the cleaning process on a very unhappy Randall!

The end

Grrrrr!

HIDDEN MONSTER

Which monster is hidden in this picture? Once you've coloured him in, write his name below.

1 Colour in the shapes marked with a dot to reveal who's hiding here!

2 Write the name of the hidden monster here!

Mike

42

Trace over the letters below to write the names of these monsters' favourite colours. Then colour the paint splodges to match.

green

red

yellow

blue

1. One day, Sulley was having a great scare shift at Monsters, Inc. "Look at all the screams Sulley's collected!" Mike proudly told a group of Scarers.

2. "Ummm, I don't see any scream cans, Mike," one Scarer replied. He was right. The cans had been taken by sneaky Randall!

3. Mike couldn't see Randall, because he had blended in with the scare floor. "Hey!" Mike shouted, "Someone stop those runaway cans!"

4. Just then, Sulley arrived back on the scare floor. "How are things going so far, Mike?" he asked. "Not so well, Sulley, our screams are escaping!" Mike cried.

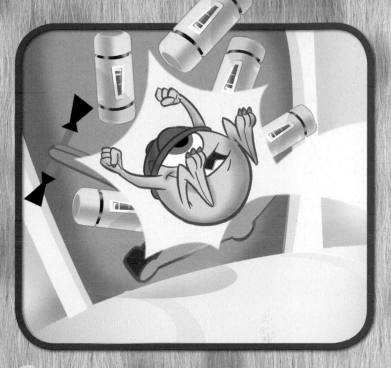

5. "No problem, pal! Get ready for a fun ride," Sulley replied. He picked up Mike, just like a bowling ball. "Move out of the way, Scarers!" he laughed.

6. "Wheee!" Mike cried, as he rolled across the scare floor. He rolled straight into the escaping scream cans, knocking them over like bowling pins!

7. Randall was trapped under the cans that Mike had knocked over! "Thanks, Randall. I needed the bowling practice for the game tonight!" Sulley joked.

8. That evening, Sulley and Mike went to the Monster Bowling Alley. "Bowling is great fun," Sulley said to his friend. "Yeah, especially when I'm the ball!" Mike agreed.

The end

SCARY SUMS

Sulley and his friends have each collected a different number of screams. Can you do the sums to work out which door each monster went through?

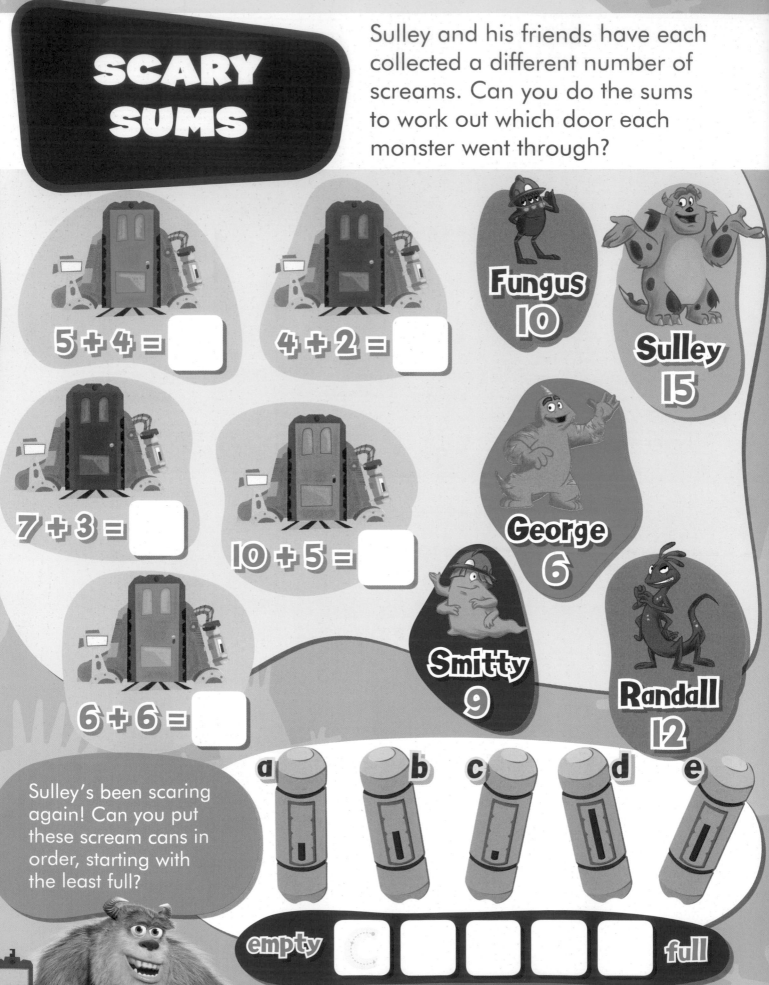

5 + 4 =

4 + 2 =

7 + 3 =

10 + 5 =

6 + 6 =

Fungus 10

Sulley 15

George 6

Smitty 9

Randall 12

Sulley's been scaring again! Can you put these scream cans in order, starting with the least full?

a b c d e

empty full

46

Answers on page 66.

Find out what Mike's message is by putting the cans in order, starting with the fullest. Write the matching letters below the cans at the bottom of the page.

MIKE'S MESSAGE

a c r e s

Answer on page 66.

SCARE SIMULATOR

Sulley is practising his scare technique in this simulator! Can you answer these teasers before he fills up a scream can?

1 Can you find these three boats in the picture?

2 Who is looking through the window?

3 Point to two teddy bears!

4 Draw over the letters to see the noise Sulley makes.

roar

5 What number is on the boy's t-shirt?

6 Can you colour this wheel the same colours as the wheels on the racing car toy?

7 Are there more red buttons or green buttons on the desk?

red   green

49

Answers on page 66.

SULLEY'S ROAR

1. One sunny day, Sulley and Mike were on their way to work. "Let's see if we can make the highest scare total ever today!" said Sulley.

2. "No problem! We can do it, buddy!" chuckled Mike. Just then, Sulley noticed a sad monster mum in her garden.

3. "What's wrong?" Sulley asked her. "My little monster's school uniform is still wet. By the time it's dry enough to wear, he'll be late!" she groaned.

4. "Stand back!" said Sulley. He took a deep breath and roared at the uniform. The blast dried it in seconds. "Thanks!" cheered the happy mum.

5. A little further along the road, Sulley and Mike met some builders. They were having trouble knocking down a wall. "Stand back!" Sulley told them.

6. He let out another enormous roar. The force was so strong that the wall crumbled into a thousand little pieces! "What a guy!" clapped the workers.

7. When Sulley and Mike finally got to work, all the roaring had made Sulley's throat sore. "Without your roar, you can't scare!" panicked Mike.

8. As Sulley went through the first door of the day, Mike was sure they'd have a low scare total. "We'll be lucky to fill one can," he sighed.

9. But Sulley had an idea. His throat was too sore to do the jump and growl so, when the child opened his eyes, Sulley whispered, "Roar!" instead.

10. The surprised child let out a very loud scream. "Even with a tiny roar, you're still the best Scarer in the business!" cheered Mike.

The end

ABOUT THE STORY

1. How did Sulley dry the little monster's uniform?

2. Who did Sulley help next?

3. What happened to Sulley's throat?

4. Did Sulley scare the child in the end?

Answers on page 66.

These monsters are messing around on a scare floor. Add lots of colour to the picture!

SPLAT!

Can you spot this cupcake in the scene?

How many monsters can you count?

UNLUCKY GEORGE

George is the unluckiest monster at Monsters, Inc. Maybe today will be different ...

One morning, George Sanderson woke up feeling strange.

"Something feels different about today. With my luck it's probably going to turn out bad," he thought.

George had good reason to worry. He had been contaminated more times than any other monster in the history of Monsters, Inc. And his fur had only just grown back after his last decontamination by the Child Detection Agency!

"If I'm extra careful, no-one will know how unlucky I feel," he told himself. However, when he walked into the Monsters, Inc. building, he heard some workers whispering about him.

"Here he comes," said one.
"Pretend you haven't seen him."

"Are you talking about me?" asked George. The two workers gulped, shook their heads and scurried away.

When George reached a scare floor things got worse. He realised that all the other Scarers were watching him. Every time he looked at them, they quickly turned away.

"They're waiting for me to get contaminated again!" muttered George.

Just then, Sulley went past, pushing a big crate. He pretended he hadn't seen George either.

"Not you as well. I thought you were my friend!" George said sadly.

"What are you talking about?" blushed Sulley.

"Admit it! Everyone is avoiding me because I'm unlucky," said George.

"Sorry George, I can't stop as I've got an important job to do, but I'll see you later," Sulley replied.

George got ready to collect a scream. "I don't care if no one likes me. I'm not getting contaminated today!" he announced.

The door opened and George leapt through it. He then did a great job of scaring a little boy. Before he returned to the scare floor, George double checked his fur for any socks or toys.

"Look everyone, I'm clean!" cheered George, as he leapt back through the door.

He was shocked to find the scare floor empty, though. "They were so sure I'd be contaminated that they've already gone," George gasped. Then an alarm went off!

"Arrghh! I must really be unlucky," he cried, as a big crowd walked towards him. Thinking it was the C.D.A., George begged, "Please don't shave me again."

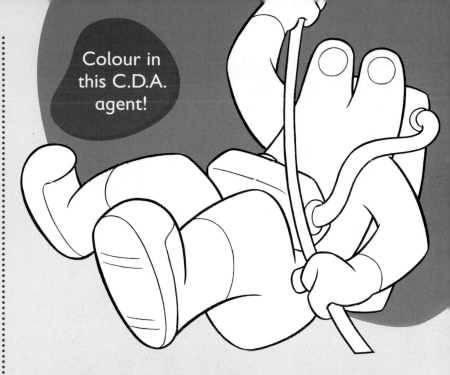

Colour in this C.D.A. agent!

Then, he saw candles, and a cake ...

"Surprise! Do you think we'd forget your birthday?" laughed Sulley, as the whole of Monsters, Inc. sang 'Happy Birthday' to him.

"My birthday? Of course! I knew today felt different!" smiled George.

As they celebrated George realised he wasn't unlucky at all. "Having friends like you makes me a very lucky monster!" he said.

The end

How many candles can you count on the cake?

Answer on page 66.

MESSY MONSTERS

Sulley and Boo have made a mess! Can you add some messy colours, too?

ODORANT

Can you find this object in the scene?

58

Answers on page 66.

It's snowing in Monstropolis! Can you spot five changes in picture B, before the snowball fight finishes?

SNOW ATTACK

A

B

Colour a splat each time you find a change.

Circle the smallest snowflake!

a

b

c

d

e

Answers on page 66.

FROSTY FUN!

Mike and Sulley are visiting Yeti, the Abominable Snowman! Answer these chilly questions.

1 How many red scarves can you count?

2 Are there more cakes on the plate or on the ground?

60

Answers on page 66.

The monsters like to play in the snow. Today they are having a snowball fight!

a

1 How many snowballs can you count on each monster?

b

c

d

e

a **b** **c** **d**

2 Can you put these snowballs in order, starting with the biggest?

BIGGEST   SMALLEST

Answers on page 66.

A MONSTER TREE

1. One night, Mike tumbled into a room to make a child laugh. He was about to tell his favourite joke when he saw something wonderful through the window.

2. It was a tree that was so pretty it made Mike feel warm inside. He quickly told the joke and rushed back to tell Sulley about the tree.

3. "It sounds like you saw a Christmas tree!" Sulley told his friend. "It's a shame you don't see trees like that growing in Monstropolis," Mike sighed.

4. "I know someone who can help me surprise Mike," Sulley thought. So, he sneaked off and called down a special door from the vault.

5. Sulley stepped into a snowy land, where the Abominable Snowman lived. When he heard Mike's wish, the snowman pulled a big tree from the ground.

6. "Thanks! Now I just have to decorate it!" Sulley said. Happy to have helped, the Abominable Snowman watched Sulley head back into Monstropolis.

WOW!

7. When he was finished, Sulley couldn't wait to show Mike the Christmas tree. "Wow, thanks! Now it feels more like Christmas in Monstropolis," Mike shouted happily.

8. Everyone agreed that the tree looked amazing! The Abominable Snowman had given the monsters the best Christmas tree Monstropolis had ever seen!

ANSWERS

PAGE 13 SCARY SHADOW MATCH
A-3, B-1, C-2, D-4

PAGE 14 MAZE RACE

PAGE 22-23 SPOT THE DIFFERENCE

PAGE 24 MONSTER MATCH-UPS
A - Don, B - Mike, C - Art, D - Terri & Terry, E - Squishy, F - Sulley.

PAGE 25 MONSTER COUNT

Carrie - 3, Don - 4, Johnny - 5, Roy - 2, Carla -3, Rosie - 3.

PAGE 27 FLAG MATCH

PAGE 27 MONSTER PARTY
The JOX are having a party.

PAGE 28 WHO'S SCARIEST?
Most Scary = Sulley. Least Scary = Mike.

PAGE 31 ODD MONSTER OUT
Sulley's nose is a different colour, the logo is missing from Mike's hat, Randy's tail is a different colour, the stripes are missing on Johnny's jumper.

PAGE 38-39 MEET THE MONSTERS
There are 6 cans.

PAGE 42 HIDDEN MONSTER
Mike is hidden in the picture.

PAGE 46 SCARY SUMS
5+4=9 (Smitty), 4+2=6 (George), 7+3=10 (Fungus), 10+5=15 (Sulley), 6+6=12 (Randall). Scream cans from empty to full = c, a, b, e, d.

PAGE 47 MIKE'S MESSAGE
Mike's message is 'scare'.

PAGE 48-49 SCARE SIMULATOR
There's a boat by the door, the window and on the bottom shelf. Mike is looking through the window. The teddy bears are on the top shelf. Number 5 is on the boy's shirt. The wheels on the racing car are grey and blue. There are more green buttons on the desk.

PAGE 52 ABOUT THE STORY
1. Sulley roared at the uniform, 2. Next he helped some builders, 3. The roaring made Sulley's throat sore, 4. Yes.

PAGE 55 SPLAT!
The monster at the front is holding the cupcake behind his back. There are 5 monsters.

PAGE 57 UNLUCKY GEORGE
There are 6 candles on the cake.

PAGE 58 MESSY MONSTERS
The soap dispenser is by the sink.

PAGE 59 SNOW ATTACK

d is the smallest snowflake.

PAGE 60-61 FROSTY FUN!
There are 4 red scarves. There are more cakes on the ground than on the plate. Yeti's face is on the igloo. The hammer is next to Mike. The word in the snow is igloo. Picture c is not in the scene.

PAGE 62 SNOWY MONSTERS
1. a - 6, b - 7, c - 5, d - 4, e - 8.
2. From biggest to smallest the snowballs are d, b, a, c.

ARCHIE THE SCARE PIG
He's hiding on pages 9, 12, 22, 24, 31, 39, 42, 47, 59, 65.

READER SURVEY

We'd love to know what you think about your Disney Pixar Monsters University Annual.

Please ask your parent/guardian to complete this form and post it to the address at the end by 28th February 2014, or you can fill in the survey online at:
www.egmont.co.uk/disneymonunisurvey2014

ONE LUCKY READER WILL WIN £150 OF BOOK TOKENS.
FIVE RUNNERS-UP WILL WIN A £25 BOOK TOKEN EACH.

NATIONAL BOOK tokens

1. WHO BOUGHT THIS ANNUAL?

- ☐ Me
- ☐ Parent/guardian
- ☐ Grandparent
- ☐ Other (please specify)

_____

2. WHY DID THEY BUY IT?

- ☐ Christmas present
- ☐ Birthday present
- ☐ I'm a collector
- ☐ Other (please specify)

_____

3. WHAT ARE YOUR FAVOURITE PARTS OF THE ANNUAL?

Stories	☐	Really like	☐	Like	☐ Don't like
Puzzles	☐	Really like	☐	Like	☐ Don't like
Colouring	☐	Really like	☐	Like	☐ Don't like
Character profiles	☐	Really like	☐	Like	☐ Don't like
Posters	☐	Really like	☐	Like	☐ Don't like
Drawing	☐	Really like	☐	Like	☐ Don't like

4. DO YOU THINK THE STORIES ARE TOO LONG, TOO SHORT OR ABOUT RIGHT?

- ☐ Too long
- ☐ Too short
- ☐ About right

5. DO YOU THINK THE ACTIVITIES ARE TOO HARD, TOO EASY OR ABOUT RIGHT?

- ☐ Too hard
- ☐ Too easy
- ☐ About right

MIKE

SULLEY

6. APART FROM MIKE AND SULLEY, WHO ARE YOUR FAVOURITE CHARACTERS?

1. _____
2. _____
3. _____

7. WHICH OTHER ANNUALS HAVE YOU BOUGHT THIS YEAR?

1. _____
2. _____
3. _____

DIVISIONAL WINNER

8. WHAT IS YOUR FAVOURITE ...

1. ... app? _____
2. ... website? _____
3. ... console game? _____
4. ... magazine? _____
5. ... book? _____

9. WHAT ARE YOUR FAVOURITE TV PROGRAMMES?

1. _____
2. _____
3. _____

10. HAVE YOU BOUGHT A DISNEY ANNUAL BEFORE? IF SO, WHICH ONES?

1. _____
2. _____
3. _____

11. WOULD YOU LIKE TO GET ANOTHER DISNEY ANNUAL AGAIN NEXT YEAR?

☐ Yes
☐ No
Why? _____
_____

THANK YOU!
(Please ask your parent/guardian to complete)

Child's name: _____ Age: _____ Boy/Girl

Parent/guardian name: _____

Parent/guardian signature: _____

Parent/guardian email address: _____

Daytime telephone number: _____

☐ Please send me the Egmont Monthly Catch-Up Newsletter.
Please cut out this form and post to: Monsters University Annual Reader Survey,
Egmont UK Limited, The Yellow Building, 1 Nicholas Road, London, W11 4AN

GOOD LUCK!